D1356596

The Mayor of Uglyville's Dilemma

The Mayor of Uglyville's Dilemma

And other mathematical puzzles and enigmas

IAN STEWART

Prospect

Atlantic Books
London

First published in hardback in Great Britain in 2005
by Atlantic Books.
Atlantic Books is an imprint of Grove Atlantic Ltd.

The pieces and illustrations first appeared in Prospect magazine.
The publishers are grateful to Prospect for permission to reproduce
the puzzles and to Stuart Brill for permission to reproduce the illustrations.

9 8 7 6 5 4 3 2 1

A CIP record for this book is available from the British Library.

ISBN 1 84354 475 X

Design by Helen Ewing
Printed and bound in Great Britain by William Clowes Ltd, Beccles, Suffolk

Atlantic Books
Ormond House
26–27 Boswell Street
London
WC1N 3JZ

Contents

....

Preface

When I was thirteen I acquired a copy of Henry Ernest Dudeney's *Amusements in Mathematics*. Dudeney was England's greatest puzzle-maker and he had a flourishing rivalry with his American counterpart, Sam Lloyd, which drove them both to produce some of the world's best puzzles: the Wapshaw's Wharf Mystery, the Leap-Year Ladies, the Educated Frogs, Mrs Perkins's Quilt... I've loved puzzles ever since, especially those that can be solved by a simple but elusive insight, an 'Aha!' moment in which the little light bulb over your skull suddenly switches on.

Late in 2002, David Goodhart, editor of *Prospect*, invited me to write a puzzle column for the magazine. He wanted, he told me, something challenging, mathematically significant and accessible to anyone. Despite a persistent feeling that this was a bit like trying to fit four elephants into a mini, I found the offer impossible to refuse. I'd just finished a twelve-year stint writing the mathematical recreations column for *Scientific American* and its sister magazines, so the puzzle part of my brain had lost its main outlet. The pressure was building up. And so 'Enigmas and Puzzles' was born.

There's always a sharp learning curve with these things. The first column erred too much on the side of mathematical significance, and too little on the accessible. By the second column it had dawned on me that I needed characters and a story line – all the usual paraphernalia of recreational mathematicians since a Babylonian scribe incised the following into a slab of wet clay: 'I found a stone but did not weigh it. After I added one seventh and one eleventh it weighed 60 *gin*. What was the original weight of the stone?'.

The answer, by the way, is $48^{1}/_{8}$, but that's not quite my point. From men digging holes in the road to water pouring out of baths that are simultaneously being filled from a tap (why?); from sacks of grain to barrels of honey; from tethered goats grazing in circular fields to desert nomads inheriting fractions of a camel, mathematics has always been made more palatable by a solid dose of narrative. And so a logic puzzle became the Green Socks Murder, the bleeping Squaresbournes attempted to work out how many children they had, democratic pirates voted on how to share their loot, and a typical American Mayor got to exercise his political machine on the good citizens of Uglyville.

That was 'accessible' taken care of, then.

'Significant' was surprisingly easy: many of the puzzles conceal an important point about mathematics or the way in which it can be applied. I'll give you just one example. The 'proportional misrepresentation' in the state of Rigvotia is based on Arrow's Paradox, discovered by the Nobel-winning mathematical economist Kenneth Arrow. This says that if you write down a list of the sensible features that any fair voting system ought to have, then they contradict each other. This is a mathematician's way of saying that you can't please everyone.

That left 'challenging', and here I need to reassure you that I don't mean 'impossibly difficult'. Some mathematical challenges have been around for centuries. The Kepler Conjecture, first posed in 1611, remained unsolved until 1998. The problem is to prove that the most efficient way to pack spheres together is what every greengrocer does with oranges every day. The answer is easy; it's proving that it's *right* that's hard. No puzzle in this book takes 387 years to solve, I promise. Neither will they take gigabytes of computer memory or teraflops of calculations. Every puzzle can be solved using the traditional tools of pencil, paper and that gadget between the ears. As a general rule, the more complicated the puzzle looks, the easier it is to solve – provided you keep a clear head.

Within these pages lurk logic puzzles, numerical puzzles, geometric puzzles, even word puzzles. Some are old favourites recast in a modern setting (the word 'stolen' is too insulting to deserve a riposte, and anyway all puzzle-designers pay due tribute to their predecessors). Some are genuine pieces of mathematics thinly or thickly disguised, and some are my own invention. Mathematics is the jewel in humanity's intellectual crown, the cherry on the cake of knowledge, the little nutty bits inside the chocolate of wisdom. I think it's important to be serious about mathematics, but 'serious' does not equate to 'solemn', as that Babylonian scribe knew well.

This is a book to exercise that gadget between your ears. Rack your brains until they resemble spaghetti, entertain family and friends with little-known mathematical factoids, challenge them to match your superlative wit and mental acuity, and be amazed by how simple it all is when you know the answer – enjoy.

Ian Stewart
Coventry, September 2005

Puzzles and Enigmas

THE MAYOR OF UGLYVILLE'S DILEMMA

The mayor of Uglyville, Texas, has decided to develop an area of run-down real estate comprising 40 city blocks in a 5x8 rectangle. Of these, 39 consist of old tenements, which will be easy (and cheap) to demolish. But one block, right in the southeast corner of the development zone, is an industrial area contaminated by large amounts of toxic waste, and whichever company has to demolish that block will risk heavy losses.

Two companies, DynaMight and Rekkit, are competing for the contract to demolish the entire zone, and the mayor can't decide which of them should get it, so he awards it to them both – with one stipulation.

'Guys, I want you to take turns. One of you must choose a road that runs right across the zone – either north-south or east-west – and demolish all the blocks on one side of it, like this, say.'

'Naturally, you'll avoid the contaminated block if you can. Then the other one chooses another road and does the same for the remaining area, and you keep taking turns until the whole development zone is flattened. Whoever has to demolish the block with all the toxic waste is gonna lose money, but I guarantee the other guy'll make a humongous profit!'

With the contract agreed, the two CEOs tossed a coin, and Rekkit got to make the first choice. Which collection of blocks should Rekkit demolish first, and why?

Answer on page 73

THE GREEN SOCKS MURDER

In *The Sign of Four* Sherlock Holmes famously said: 'When you have eliminated the impossible, whatever remains, however improbable, must be the truth.' A striking success for this method occurred in the little-known green socks murder.

A football referee, Brendan Black, was found dead – strangled, with a green sock still tied round his neck. A trail of clues led Holmes to just three suspects: George Green, Bill Brown, and Wally White. All were keen amateur football players. Holmes knew that one played for Dipswitch City, another played for Liverwurst Wranglers, and the third played for Tottering Tuesday – but his enquiries failed to reveal who played for which team. He did know that each team's official strip consisted of shirt, shorts, and (significantly) socks. Moreover, each team's strip comprised one green garment, one brown, and one white – counting 'socks' as a single garment. Nobody wore odd socks, of course.

Subtle traces at the scene of the crime made it clear to Holmes that the murderer had used one of his own football socks to strangle the unfortunate official. Moreover, the great detective could prove that the murder must have been committed by one of the three suspects. Witnesses informed him that between them the three players wore one shirt of each colour, one pair of shorts of each colour, and one pair of socks of each colour. None of them wore two or more garments of the same colour. Holmes immediately realised that each of the suspects must have worn exactly one garment with the same colour as his name. That is, White wore precisely one white garment, Brown wore one brown garment, and Green wore one green garment.

Discreet enquiries by Dr Watson dug up further useful information:

1. These three garments were either all the same type (for example, all shirts) or all different (shirt, shorts, socks).

2. Brown's socks were the same colour as White's shirt.

3. The person whose name was the colour of White's shorts wore socks whose colour was the name of the person wearing a white shirt.

4. The colour of Green's socks was the same as the name of the person wearing the same colour shorts as the shirt worn by the person whose name was the colour of Brown's socks.

'It's no use, Holmes,' said a baffled Watson. 'We cannot find the killer.'

'On the contrary, my dear Watson. The deduction is elementary.'

'Then who was the criminal?'

'You know my methods,' said Holmes enigmatically.

•••

Answer on page 74

YO-HO-HO AND A DEMOCRATIC VOTE

'Shiver me gudgeons and caulk the dogwatch, but here's plunder to cringle any man's futtock-plate!' Short Jim Pewter poured gold coins from hand to hook in glee. He was captain of the pirate ship *Pretty Polly*, and the nine other crewmembers knew that he was the fiercest pirate on board. In fact, they all knew exactly who was fiercer than whom, and no two pirates were equally fierce, so there was a precise pecking-order. The *Pretty Polly* had just completed a successful attack on a schooner bound from Cádiz, and their haul was 100 gold pieces, each a single gleaming coin.

'Ahaargh, lads,' snarled Pewter with an evil grin. 'You all knows I keeps a tight ship, an' a fair one, ahaargh!' He brandished his cutlass. 'So we'll split the loot in our usual democratic piratical way, right mates?' The crew cheered – Pewter was, after all, the fiercest pirate, and they always cheered anything he said.

'As Cap'n, I opens the bidding. I'll make a perposal about 'ow we does the division, and then we all votes on it, ahaargh – one vote each, including me. If half of us or more say "aye", the perposal passes, and that's 'ow we split the loot. Otherwise you lads toss me overboard to feed the sharks – and the next fiercest pirate is elected Cap'n and makes a new perposal… and so on until somebody's perposal passes.'

The crew cheered again. They all liked throwing people overboard, but they liked hard cash even better. Naturally, they were not keen to be thrown overboard themselves. All the pirates were rational, knew that the other pirates were rational, knew that they knew that… and so on. They also knew that the gold pieces must be considered indivisible, and that there was no point in making agreements to share pieces, because no pirate could trust his shipmates to stick to the bargain.

What division of spoils should Pewter propose, to avoid becoming shark-bait and secure himself as much loot as possible?

Hint: work backwards from the last two pirates, assuming that the voting ever gets that far. All pirates can work out what this scenario implies. Here are the first few steps. Call the

12

pirates P1, P2,... P10 in increasing order of ferocity, so P10 = Pewter. If the voting ever gets to the point where only P1 and P2 are left on board, then P2 can (and will) propose to keep all the loot for himself, and P1 can't outvote him. Next, suppose that only P3, P2, and P1 remain on board. Now P1 knows – and P3 knows that he knows – that if P3's proposal is voted down, P1 will get nothing. So P1 will vote in favour of anything that P3 proposes, provided it yields P1 more than nothing. P3 therefore bribes P1 by proposing that P1 gets one gold piece, P2 gets nothing, while P3 gets the other 99. Now suppose that the voting gets down to just P4, P3, P2, and P1...

Answer on page 74

HAT TRICK

••

When Alfie, Betty and Gemma were chosen to appear on
Who Wants to Challenge the Weakest Date? they had been
very excited, but now that the moment of truth was
approaching, all three of them were feeling distinctly queasy.
Especially when the host explained the rules to them.

'This is a team game. When your turn comes, I am going
to place a hat on each of your heads. The hats will be either
black or white, chosen at random with equal probabilities.
You will not be able to see your own hat, but you will be able
to see the hats of the other two players.

'You will be given ten seconds to think about your choice,
and then each of you will simultaneously do one of three
things. You may (a) pass, (b) state that your hat is white, or
(c) state that your hat is black. If you all pass, or if one or
more of you makes a false statement about their hat colour,
you all lose. If at least one of you does not pass, and
everyone who does not pass guesses their own hat colour
correctly, then you win £1m each.

'During the game itself, you will be in sealed booths,
unable to communicate with each other, but able to see each
other's faces and hats on a monitor. Your choices will be
stored electronically until all three of you have chosen, and
only then will you choices be revealed. Your choice of
strategy, now, will determine how good your chances are. You
have five minutes to confer.'

'We may as well all guess,' said Alfie. 'It's random, right?'

'No,' said Gemma. 'That way, we all have to get the answer right, a chance of one in eight. We should elect one of us to guess, and the other two should pass. Then our chances improve to one in two.'

'Right,' said Alfie. 'We can't do any better than that if it's random.'

'I think we can,' said Betty. 'I think there's a strategy that gives us a three in four chance of winning.'

Was she right?

•••

Answer on page 75

SQUARED SQUARES

It is easy to make a rectangle out of nine equal square tiles – just fit them together in a 3x3 array. But can you make a rectangle out of nine *different* square tiles? And what about making a *square* out of different square tiles?

The first 'squared rectangle' was published in 1925 by Z Moroń, and it used ten square tiles of sizes 3, 5, 6, 11, 17, 19, 22, 23, 24, 25. Soon after, he found one with just nine square tiles, the smallest number possible, which looks like this:

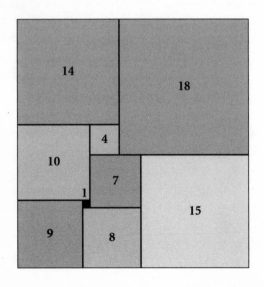

For many years, mathematicians thought that making a square out of different sized square tiles was impossible, but in 1939 RP Sprague proved them wrong, by finding 55 distinct square tiles that fit together to make a (rather large) square. In 1940, four mathematicians (RL Brooks, CAB Smith, AH Stone and WT Tutte) published a famous paper relating the problem to electrical networks – the connection is not obvious, but the idea is that the network determines how the squares fit together and how big they are. They found other solutions by this method.

In 1948, TH Willcocks found 24 squares that fit together to make a square. Until recently it was thought that no smaller set would do the job, but in 1962, AJW Duijvestijn used a computer to show that only 21 square tiles are needed, and this is the minimum number. Their sizes are 2, 4, 6, 7, 8, 9, 11, 15, 16, 17, 18, 19, 24, 25, 27, 29, 33, 35, 37, 42, and 50.

Here are two questions for you.

1. How do Moroń's ten tiles fit together? Hint: the rectangle has size 47x65.

2. How do Duijvestijn's 21 squares fit together? They make a fascinating jigsaw puzzle – or a patio.

If you want a really hard one: is it possible to tile the entire infinite plane, leaving no gaps, using exactly one tile of each whole number size: 1, 2, 3, 4… ? But be warned: nobody knows the answer.

Answer on page 76

NUMEROMANCER

Conjuring up a demon is a delicate business, especially when the demon in question is Devilspawn the Unwashable, but Magister Bumblebore was confident in his grasp of the arcane arts of sorcery. Recalling what had once happened to his friend Faustus, he concentrated on making sure that the pentacle inscribed on the floor of his thaumaturgatorium was complete and accurate in every tiny detail.

Bumblebore was a sorcerer, skilled in numeromancy – the use of arithmetical and geometrical figures for magical effect. He was trying to construct a pentacle, a five-pointed star, because five was Devilspawn's talismanic number. But this had to be a special pentacle – one decorated with magic numbers. A pentacle has five vertices, plus five more special points where its edges cross; each edge contains precisely four of these portentous points. Bumblebore had set himself the task of placing the numbers from 1 to 10 on the ten points, using each exactly once, so that along any edge the four numbers that occurred would add up to the same magic total.

He had calculated that if such an arrangement were possible, then its 'magic constant' – the aforesaid total – would be 22. He could *almost* see how to do that, but somehow it never quite worked… At this point, his apprentice rushed in carrying several mops, with the news that in an ancient grimoire, the *Polynomnicon*, he had found a cunning proof that no such arrangement can exist.

Ignoring the raw magic crackling off the pages of the ancient tome, Bumblebore searched the proof for flaws, but found none. His face fell.

'The grimoire does speak, Magister, of an arrangement with magic constant 24.'

'Indeed, there is such a configuration,' replied the sorcerer. 'But mark ye well, young apprentice, and learn the subtleties of numeromancy. The *Polynomnicon* was written by the Dark Lady Volderman, and her arrangement uses the numbers 1, 2, 3, 4, 5, 6, 8, 9, 10, and 12. Neither 7 nor 11 occurs, so the sequence is *broken*. The demon could escape through the numerological gap, and wreak havoc on the world!'

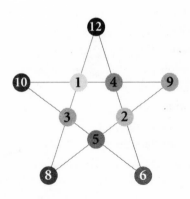

Bumblebore grimaced in frustration. 'We must therefore scrub Devilspawn the Unwashable –'

'You can't, Magister. That is *why* he is unwash –'

'Any more of your backchat, Harold my lad, and I'll have you mucking out the behemoth-shed again! Since a perfect pentagram does not exist, a substitute must be found! Possibly a magic – uh – hexacle? A six-pointed star? Then I can summon Gorgonzolia the Abominable Weremaid, whose talismanic number is 6. But if you value your life, there must be no breaks in the numeric sequence!'

Can you help Bumblebore by placing the numbers 1–12 at the marked points, using one of each, to make the six lines all add to the same total? This time the task is possible. The magic constant must be 26. There are 80 different solutions, and in 12 of them the six outermost star points also add to the magic constant 26.

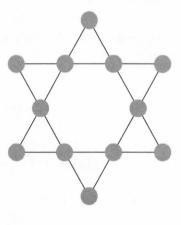

Answer on page 77

PROPORTIONAL MISREPRESENTATION

It was election time in the Democratic Autocracy of Rigvotia, and the ruling Dictatorial-Democratic party was in trouble. An economic slump had forced Rigvotia to join the Subsidised Trade Alliance, whose member states insisted on the transferable ranking electoral system.

In this system, each voter ranked the political parties in order, and all subsequent decisions were based on those rankings. If any party was ranked first by more than 50 per cent of the voters, that party won. If not, two parties were chosen at random, and their rankings were compared across all voters. Whichever party lost was then eliminated, and the process continued with the remaining parties.

Rigvotia had three political parties. When the votes were counted, 49 per cent of the electorate preferred the Paternalists, 49 per cent preferred the Autocrats, and only 2 per cent preferred the DicDems.

'We've lost,' said the president. 'I shall declare a state of emergency –'

'Perhaps,' mused his minister for graft, 'that will not be necessary. Both of our opponents have less than 50 per cent of the vote, so there must be a run-off.'

'Look at the figures, man! It's a disaster!'

'I have looked. The results are curious. The 2 per cent who rank us first all rank the Autocrats second. The 49 per cent who rank the Autocrats first all rank the Paternalists second.

And the 49 per cent who rank the Paternalists first all rank us second.'

'I don't see how that helps. I will order the secret democratic police –'

'There's no need. All you have to do is rig the choice of parties for the run-off.'

Which two parties must take part in the run-off to ensure that the DicDems are elected?

Answer on page 77

FLATLAND CHESS

Flatland is a Euclidean plane, and its creatures are confined to two dimensions. The men are polygons and the women are lines. Victoria Line is playing Flatland draughts with her friend Dilly. The board for this traditional game is eight cells long. Each player has three pieces, and at the start, they are arranged like this:

Players take turns to move a piece: black pieces can only move to the right and white pieces to the left. A piece can either move one cell forward, if the destination is empty, or it can jump over an opposing piece into an empty cell, removing the piece that is jumped over. A move may consist of a series of jumps, and jumps are compulsory if they are possible.

'You move first,' said Victoria graciously. 'You're the guest.' But Dilly was adamant that Victoria, as hostess, should have the honour of the first move. Were they being polite, or did they know that moving second offers an advantage?

Unable to agree who should start, they decided to play chess instead. The Flatland version uses the same board as draughts, and each player has three pieces: king, knight, and rook. The rules are very like Spaceland chess. All three pieces can move in either direction. Any move terminates either on an empty cell, or on a cell occupied by an enemy piece, which is removed from the board ('taken'). A rook can move across any number of unoccupied cells. A king moves only one cell at a time, and cannot move into 'check' – a cell that is already threatened by the enemy. A knight moves by jumping over an adjacent cell, which may be empty or occupied. If a player has no legal moves available, the game is 'stalemate' and drawn. If a player can threaten the opposing king, and the king cannot escape, then that is 'checkmate' and the game is won. The initial position is like this:

If Victoria wants to make sure she wins, should she choose to play first, or second? Or can one of the players force a draw?

Answer on page 78

CHANCE ENCOUNTER

· ·

Matthew M Maddox, known as 'Matt' to his friends, is living proof that mathematics can be a profitable area of activity if you go about it the right way. A typical Maddox ploy took place on a recent train journey from Clapham Junction to Wandsworth Town. To while away the time, Maddox engaged two fellow passengers in conversation. Soon they were playing cards, for cash, and the game had been suggested by Maddox.

'OK Mark and Patsy, here are the rules,' said Maddox. 'We use just the four aces from the pack. I'll be banker, you two can bet against me. Patsy, suppose it's your turn. You and I each lay a pound coin on the table. Mark deals the four cards face down in a row. Then Patsy chooses two of the four cards, and marks them with the two coins. Mark then turns Patsy's chosen cards face up. Notice that I never touch the cards, so I can't play any tricks on you. If both aces have the same colour, Patsy wins and takes the cash. If the colours are different, I win. Then it's Patsy's turn to deal and Mark's turn to choose, and we keep playing until we either reach Wandsworth Town station or one of us runs out of money.

'Obviously it's a fair game,' Maddox finished. 'Either the two cards have the same colour, or they don't. It's 50-50.'

'I agree it's fair,' said Patsy, 'but not for that reason. There are four possibilities: red/red, red/black, black/red, or black/black. In two cases I win, in two I lose. So it is 50-50, but there are four cases, not two.'

'Patsy's right, and I definitely think we should play,' said Mark. He sounded a bit too eager. He had worked out that the game was to his advantage. The order in which the cards were chosen didn't make any difference, so there were neither two cases nor four, but three: both red, both black, or one of each. And in two of those cases, the banker would lose. Their chance of winning was 2 in 3! They would clean up.

Two answers, three reasons for them. Which was right?

••

Answer on page 78

THE ROUTE OF THE MATTER

'Let me look at that map!'

'You can look at it as long as you like, Alice – but you won't find a route,' said Henry, with his usual irritating certitude.

The map showed their home town, Nodding Donkey, their destination Eastward Hoe, a rather disreputable seaside town, and all of the local towns and roads.

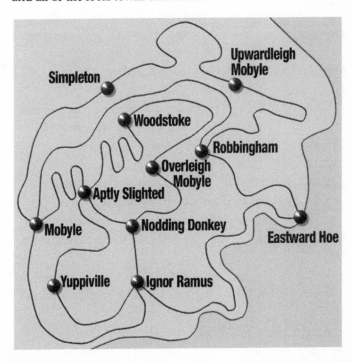

'It's easy,' Alice said. 'Take the M666 motorway to Ignor Ramus and then the coastal road to Eastward Hoe. It's the B1066, I think –'

'No, we can't do that,' Henry insisted. 'We agreed to visit our nephew Onslow in Yuppiville on the way.'

'Oh yes – so we go via Aptly Slighted to Yuppiville, next to Ignor Ramus and then we take the coastal road to Eastward Hoe.'

'Yes, but we also promised Auntie Jezebel – the one who lives in Simpleton – that we'd take a look at her cat, Tiddles. He's been poorly, and you know how much he likes sitting on your lap… though I hope he doesn't throw up like last time. And we can't possibly visit her and not have tea with my mother in Robbingham.'

'Good point,' Alice conceded. 'And I suppose while we're in the vicinity we ought to go and see Cousin Wilberforce in Upwardleigh Mobyle. And we shouldn't forget Perdita and Granville in Woodstoke.'

'That reminds me. We said that next time we passed we'd take a bag of Perdita's rock-buns to little Britney – her mum lives in Overleigh Mobyle now she's separated from Declan. Omigod – Declan! We'll have to see him! Where is he?'

'Ouagadougou.'

'Scrub Declan, then,' Henry said. 'But we've got to visit the others.'

'Agreed,' said Alice. 'But every time we pass through a town, we'll have to visit whoever lives there. If they find out we didn't, they'll be upset. And we can't visit some of them more times than others.'

Henry grimaced. 'True. We need a route that starts from Nodding Donkey, visits each town on the map exactly once, and ends in Eastward Hoe. There must be a way.'

Alice shrugged. 'No way, I'm sure.'

Was she right?

Answer on page 79

SLOANE ARRANGER

Amanda Bander-Gander was very excited waiting for the feng-shui adept to arrive. She had felt for some time that her apartment in Sloane Square was lacking in style. Now she was going to find out what was wrong. She was especially proud of her carpet, with its elegant chess motif and its unusual shape. It had been made by joining an 8x8 chessboard to a 6x6 one.

The doorbell rang – it must be him!

'Allo, luv. I come ter do yer fung-shooey fing wotcha said on me answerphone.'

'Are you Lin Jin-li? You don't look Chinese.'

'I ain't, luv. But that's me name. Well, it's really Len Kingsley, but I uses it for trade purposes.' His eyes roved around the room. 'Nice pad! But that carpet's gotta go.'

'What's your problem with my rug?' Amanda asked frostily. 'Don't you relate to the postmodernist Kasparovian motif?'

'Motif's fine,' he said. 'But the *shape*…'

'What shape ought it to be, then?'

'Square.'

Amanda stared at him. 'But it is square.'

'Not in the usual meanin' of the term, luv.'

'You mean really square? *Plain* square?'

The feng-shui adept said nothing, and a blush spread across her throat. 'One square? Not two squarey things stuck together?'

'You got it, luv. What we in the trade calls "square".'

'I'll have to buy another one!' Amanda wailed. 'They cost a fortune!'

'Now don't you worry,' said Len. 'Wotcha got is 8 metres square plus 6 metres square, which is 100 square metres in total. So it oughta be possible to cut it up and make a 10 metre x 10 metre square.'

Amanda thought about it. 'I suppose you could cut it into 100 separate little squares. But that would be a bit messy.'

Len put a finger beside his nose. 'That's wot you 'ired me for. The expert touch. I can manage with a lot less pieces than that.'

What is the smallest number of pieces into which you can cut Amanda's carpet and make a 10x10 checkerboard pattern?

• •

Answer on page 79

THE BLEEPING SQUARESBOURNES

'Squaron?'

'Yes, Squozzy?'

'How old am I?'

'Old enough to have an awful lot of kids,' his wife replied. She was wondering why a tail was poking out of the sink.

Squozzy Squaresbourne gave this apparently new fact his undivided attention. 'How many ****ing kids have we got, doll?'

His wife Squaron decided it wasn't worth trying to extract the dog from the waste-disposal unit and gave her husband a cool stare. 'You mean you don't know?'

'I dunno how many legs I got, Squaron! How am I expected to remember kids?'

Three dishevelled cats shot past, pursued by a radio-controlled robot. Squaron didn't bat an eyelid. She was used to this. 'Try, Squozzy. How many can you remember?'

Squozzy sighed. This was unfair, it taxed the brain cell. 'Well, there's Smelly, of course. No one could forget Smelly. And Joke. I mean Jerk. Or was it –'

'Junk.'

'Yeah, right. So that's three.'

'Two. Now all you need is to remember the other seven.'

Squozzy counted on his fingers and was pleased not to run out before he'd finished. 'You mean we got nine ****ing kids?'

'At the last count, yes.'

'Oh. How old are the kids, then?'

'Don't be so boring, Dad!' screamed Smelly. 'Who cares how old the stupid little ****s are?'

'Your father cares, dear, and so should you.' She sighed as Smelly stomped off in a sulk. 'Let me see… I do remember that the children's ages are equally spaced. And the sum of the squares of their ages is the square of your age, Squozzy.'

'For ****'s sake, Squaron! Can't you give me a straight answer?'

How old is Squozzy?

Answer on page 80

LEADER OF THE PACK

....

'*We gotta move these refrigerators…*'

Darren tapped his workmate on the shoulder, stopping the song in mid-flow. 'Three objections, Mike me old mate. One: what we have to move is cordless electric window washers –'

'Yeah, but that don't fit the music. "*We gotta move these cordless electric window washers*" – no, no way,' said Mike.

'Two: your singing is atrocious. And three, you're far too old to be part of the MTV generation.'

'Aw, come on, Darren. My generation *invented* MTV.'

'Your generation invented SFA. *My* generation invented MTV. And neither is going to help us pack these boxes in the big crates, like our boss told us to do two hours ago, right?' said Darren.

'I told you: they won't fit! We can get five of them in the crate with what looks like room to spare, but the last one won't go.'

'Are you sure?'

Mike gestured in irritation. 'They're all standard sizes, Darren. The washers come in square boxes, two feet by two, and one foot high. The crates are cubes, three feet on each side.'

Darren did a quick mental calculation. 'We're supposed to get six boxes, each of volume 2x2x1=4 cubic feet, inside a crate of volume 3x3x3=27 cubic feet. So the total volume of the boxes is 24 cubic feet – which means they ought to fit in comfortably with three cubic feet to spare.'

'Right on. But when we fit the first five in, the remaining space is all higgledy-piggledy and complicated. The sixth box won't fit. No matter what we try.'

Darren scratched his head, seeking inspiration. 'It's a bit of a bummer, yeah. Unless…' He snapped his fingers. 'I know what we're doing wrong, Mike!'

'What?'

'We're trying to fit the *boxes* into the crate!'

'Darren, have you gone nuts? Of course we're trying to fit the boxes into the crate! That's what the boss told us, remember?' Mike shook his head. 'What else ought we try to pack into the crate?'

Darren gave an enigmatic grin.

How do the six boxes fit into the crate?

Answer on page 80

SQUARE-DANCING DILEMMA

In an obscure village in the depths of Bumpkinshire, the Clopswold-in-the-Midden Stick-Dancing team was rehearsing for the annual inter-village competition. Or would have been, were it not for an unfortunate lapse on the part of their Deputy Stickwangler.

'You brought the wrong set of jigging-sticks again, Josiah.'

'Can't we manage with these, Barnaby?' Josiah brandished a bundle of eight sticks: four of them two Neolithic yards long and the other four one Neolithic yard long. 'We can make squares out of them easily.' He laid them out like this:

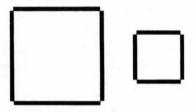

Then he began to dance an intricate jig, skipping between the squares until he trod on a stick and tripped over.

'That won't impress the judges, Josiah. Aside from that left-toed huladango when you should have been doing a gallivanting farandole, you've only laid out two squares, and they're different sizes. Rule 745.b.ii calls for three squares, all the same size.'

'Well, we can lay the sticks out some other way,' Josiah said, defensively. 'How about this?'

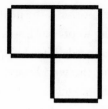

'No, there are two sticks left over. Rule 466.b.iv stipulates that you have to use all the sticks in your possession,' said Barnaby.

'I could throw two of them away.'

'That would be cheating, and according to rule 832.c.ix the penalty for that is –'

'Say no more,' said Josiah. 'I'll think of another arrangement. I'm not allowed to break them, am I?'

'No. I'd be surprised if you can find an arrangement that obeys all the rules.'

Can you help Josiah find an arrangement? Ignore the thickness of the sticks.

Answer on page 81

In the early hours of the morning, the next edition of *News Interpretational* was going to press. All was on track until the sports reporter announced: 'I need help with this headline about the round-the-world yacht race between Elaine Mercator and Arthur McLellan. I can't work out if it should be ELAINE GETS THE GLORY or ARTHUR SNEAKS HOME BY A WHISKER.'

'Tricky,' said the obituary writer, who was the only other journalist around at that moment. 'Did you look on the internet?'

'Of course, that's where I got the story from. But the report doesn't say who won. Both boats left Portsmouth at the same time, heading for Sydney, and whoever got back to Portsmouth first would win. Elaine's boat averaged 30 knots on the outward leg, but only 20 knots on the return leg because her keel fell off. Arthur's boat did a steady 24½ knots on both legs.'

'Isn't it obvious? Surely Elaine –'

'Ah, but she might have had to make a detour, losing ground. Or she might have stayed over longer in Sydney.'

The obituary writer tilted the screen to see better. 'Hmm… says here that each of them travelled exactly 18,000 nautical miles on each leg, and each stayed two days in

Sydney to make repairs and take on provisions. So no detours or delays.'

'Which means…'

'Elaine won, with a higher average speed of 25 knots.'

The sports reporter started to type in the headline, then paused. 'Are you sure?'

'Of course. Why?'

'We'll look pretty silly if it was Arthur.'

Who won, Elaine or Arthur?

• •

Answer on page 81

TRAIN OF EVENTS

In the middle of the single-track branch line from Westmouth to Eastley there is a short stretch with two lines. This section, known as Central Interchange, is approached from each end through a set of points that allows access from the single track to either of the twin tracks.

After rail privatisation, the single-line sections of track were owned, respectively, by Westnet and Eastrail, the northernmost line of Central Interchange was owned by Nortrak, and the southernmost by Southlink. This led to confusion over the timetable, and it was not unusual for two trains to arrive at Central Interchange at the same time, heading in opposite directions.

On one such occasion a green commuter train bound for Eastley, with 26 coaches and one engine, arrived at Central Interchange just as a red freight train, with 103 coaches and one engine, arrived heading for Westmouth. This unfortunate circumstance resulted in an impasse.

+ 17 coaches

WESTMOUTH

+ 93 coac

EASTLEY

Each engine driver politely suggested that the other should back up to the nearest station, where the lines again branched and it would be possible for the other to pass. These suggestions were rejected, with some heat, but eventually the drivers agreed that they would have to solve the problem by manoeuvring their trains past each other using the two tracks at Central Interchange.

The northern track is just long enough to hold six coaches, or five coaches plus an engine. The southern track is just long enough to hold seven coaches, or six coaches plus an engine. How can the two trains get past each other, with the least number of changes of direction of movement of the engines? Coaches can be uncoupled and recoupled to either train.

Answer on page 82

PUNK POODLE PARADE

Every year since 2003 the village hall at Much Grumbling has hosted the Punk Poodle Parade, an event where competitors decorate their pets with coloured dyes before an enthralled audience. The stage set consists of a row of 12 stools, of which the left hand two are empty (for the competitor and his or her poodle) and the other ten are occupied by five buckets of green dye and five buckets of purple dye, arranged alternately like this, where dark grey represents purple and light grey represents green:

Unfortunately, the stage-manager's assistant had mistakenly set them out like this:

'You'll have to rearrange those, lad. The colours have to alternate. And the two adjacent empty stools are on the wrong end.'

The assistant sighed, picked up a bucket of green dye, and placed it on the floor.

'No, lad, not like that. You'll get the floor messy if you put buckets on it. And you've got two hands, haven't you? I want you to pick up a pair of adjacent buckets, one in each hand, and transfer them to two adjacent empty stools. Don't cross your hands, though, you might drop something. Keep the buckets in the same order from left to right across the stage. And try to move as few buckets as possible, OK?'

What is the smallest possible number of moves needed to reach the correct sequence?

Answer on page 82

ORDER INTO CHAOS

'You're always rabbiting on about mathematical puzzles,' Innumeratus complained, 'but I like word games, and maths can't say anything about those. I mean, puzzles like "Change SHIP into DOCK by altering just one letter at a time, and not moving any letters, so that at each step you get a genuine word." My solution is

SHIP

SLIP

SLOP

SLOT

SOOT

LOOT

LOOK

LOCK

DOCK

but I suppose there could be a shorter one.'

'Ah,' said Mathophila. 'You mean you want the minimal path from SHIP to DOCK in the graph whose nodes are valid four-letter words and whose edges join words that are unit Hamming distance apart. I could use maths to solve that if I searched the dictionary to work out the graph.'

'You're just trying to blind me with technical terms,' protested Innumeratus. 'Anyway, that's not a theorem, just glorified trial and error.'

'True. But there is a theorem. If you change SHIP to DOCK then somewhere along the way you have to use a word with two vowels. Counting Y as a vowel. Like SOOT in your solution.'

'How can you be so sure, without working all the solutions out?'

'Every valid four-letter word has at least one vowel. If you never add a second vowel, then the vowel of SHIP stays in the third position. So it can't end up in the second position, as in DOCK,' said Mathophila. 'And while you're checking the logic, here's a mathematical word puzzle for you. Change ORDER into CHAOS. Same rules.'

••

Answer on page 83

TRICKY WICKET

I was researching the history of Wackingham Village Cricket Club, and old George, who had been a member since the club began, was recalling its high point – the final of the Krunchy Kowfeed Kup, against the feared opponents from Chuckit.

'I remember it like it was yesterday,' he said, downing a beer. 'It was a one day match, one innings per team – yes, ta, another'd be nice. Lemme see… All the runs came off the bat that day – no extras at all. Chuckit batted first, and their first seven batsmen all got ducks. Then, with the score at 0 for 7, they made a magnificent comeback. The eighth batsman scored one fifth of their total runs plus three fifths of a run. The ninth scored one quarter of their remaining runs plus three quarters of a run. The tenth scored one third of their remaining runs plus three thirds of a run. And in a massive last-wicket stand, the eleventh batsman scored half their remaining runs plus three halves of a run.

'Well, we was up against it, I can tell you. But we got off to a good start. Our opening batsman scored one twelfth of our total runs plus one twelfth of a run. The second scored one eleventh of our remaining runs plus one eleventh of a run. The third scored one tenth of our remaining runs plus one tenth of a run. The fourth scored one ninth of our remaining runs plus one ninth of a run. And the pattern continued like that… The tenth batsman scored one third of our remaining runs plus one third of a run… and in a nail-biting finish, our eleventh batsman scored half of our remaining runs plus half a run, and it was all over.'

'Um – who won?' I asked. 'What were the scores?'

'Don't have the foggiest idea,' he replied.

Answer on page 84

PROPITIOUSLY PROPORTIONED PYRAMID

Klephtnose III, an Egyptian pharaoh from the middle kingdom whose name unaccountably fails to appear on the famous king list at Abydos, had summoned his master of monuments, Amunaleg.

'As one well versed in mathematics, you know that a triangle whose sides are in the proportions 3, 4, 5 must have a right angle?'

'I am, O mighty King. For that is how your surveyors lay out such angles when surveying the land.'

'I am minded that you should build me a pyramid in similarly propitious proportions. The height, the side of the square base, and the sloping edge that leads from the corner of the base to the apex, must be in the proportions of consecutive whole numbers. And no cheating with bent

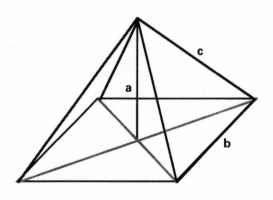

pyramids like the one you built at Dashur! Or one with stepped sides, as at Saqqara! I want all edges to be perfect straight lines, with the apex vertically above the centre of the base.'

Amunaleg's face fell. 'Your word is my command, O my King!' But his face showed fear, for he was afraid that the task would be a mathematical impossibility. 'I will do my best, O King.'

'You will do my bidding,' replied the pharaoh, who had already carried out the necessary computation, but liked to make his subjects sweat.

Which three consecutive whole numbers would make a pyramid with the right proportions?

• •

Answer on page 85

THE MERCHANT OF SAMARKAND

Each morning Ishtaq the Ingenious, a wealthy merchant of fabled Samarkand, awoke to the sound of songbirds and the scent of wild blossoms. And each morning, his bones felt older than the day before, and his heart felt heavier, for he knew that his time was nigh. And so he sent for an astrologer, to help him draw up his will.

'You should consult a notary,' said the astrologer. 'Legal matters are unworthy of my talents.'

'It is not the legal instrument, but the manner of the division, that requires your wisdom,' the merchant answered. 'I wish everything to be divided equally among my three sons.'

'Your intentions are fair,' the astrologer counselled. 'But they may not be practical. A house, for instance, is not easily divided.'

Ishtaq nodded. 'I have foreseen that difficulty, and to simplify the task I have converted all my wealth into 21 jewel-studded barrels of valuable perfume oil.'

'Then it is simple. Bequeath seven barrels to each son.'

'Not quite so simple,' Ishtaq replied. 'Seven barrels are full, seven are half full, and seven are empty.'

'Each son should receive three and a half barrels of oil,' said the astrologer. 'There are many ways to divide the oil equally.'

'Yes, but the barrels are also valuable, and they, too, must be divided equally.'

'Pour half of the oil from each full barrel into an empty one,' the astrologer suggested. 'Then you have 21 half-full barrels, and can give seven to each son.'

'Alas, the barrels are sealed to prevent spoilage and must remain so until I am dead,' Ishtaq said. 'And there is one final condition. For reasons of sacred numerology, no son may receive more than three identical barrels.'

The astrologer furrowed his brow. 'That is a puzzle worthy of my attention.'

How can the merchant divide the barrels equally between his sons?

• •

Answer on page 85

HIGH AFTERNOON

••

'Do not forsake me, oh my darling…'

The sheriff cursed, threw the stereo out of the window, and stared for the thousandth time at the clock on the wall. It was a handsome clock, with Roman numerals from I to XII and two finely crafted hands to tell the hours and minutes. No second hand, though. He didn't buy second-hand goods.

The clock read one minute past noon.

'Well, that just about wraps it up,' said his deputy. 'I guess the fight's off, huh? If I was you, boss, I'd forget her and find myself anoth –'

'No!'

'But you were going to have the shoot-out when the big hand and the little hand came together.'

'At noon, you mean?'

'It's traditional. And it looked to me as if the hands were together at noon.'

'Yes, but that wasn't when I agreed to fight. I agreed to

52

fight at the precise instant when the hands first come together again, after noon.' He cursed again. 'The trouble is, I can't work out when that will be.'

The deputy scored a direct hit on the spittoon and chewed earnestly on his wad of tobacco, deep in thought. 'Five past one,' he said.

'Not exactly,' said the sheriff. 'When the big hand is on the one, the little hand is really just past the one. One twelfth of the way to two, in fact.'

'Oh, yeah. Well, a bit later than that, then.'

'Of course. But I need to know exactly how much later. My cunning survival plan depends on absolutely precise timing.'

What time is the sheriff's fight?

••

Answer on page 86

CAT O'SEVEN TAILS

In a patch of savannah on the planet Katzwiskas, which circled the star Mu Leonis, two xenologists were tracking a pride of the indigenous felinoids. There were two species, distinguishable by how many tails each had.

'There they are!' hissed Chief Xenologist Tabitha Catt.

'I can't see them,' said her assistant Tom. 'Where are they?'

'Behind that clump of blue grass. You can see their tails clearly.'

'How many felinoids are there?'

'Well, *Catticus fatticus* always has five tails – some purple, some pink, and *Pussius fussius* always has seven – some pink, some purple. Computer: how many felinoids are consistent with the total number of tails?'

There was a brief pause. Then the ship's computer answered: 'Does not compute.'

'Sorry?'

'The total number of tails is inconsistent with any combination of *C fatticus* and *P fussius*. In fact, it is the largest possible number of tails that is inconsistent with such a combination.'

'Are any tails missing or hidden?'

'No, all felinoids are complete and all tails are gloriously upright and visible. But it does occur to me that one tail is black, and the ship's cat Sooty has gone missing.'

Assuming that one tail is Sooty's, and that the other tails belong to the two felinoid species, how many Katwiskan felinoids were there?

Answer on page 86

DIGITAL CENTURY

To celebrate the hundredth issue of *Prospect* magazine, the editor commissioned Stacy Ermine, prominent artist and winner of the celebrated Turnip Prize, to produce a suitably enlightening work. After several seconds' thought, Ermine despatched an assistant to purchase a large board and a pot of emulsion paint. While a second assistant removed the top from the pot with a hired chainsaw, a third assistant nailed the board to the wall of the editor's office. Then, under instructions from Ermine, a fourth assistant painted numerals on the board, forming a curious mathematical statement:

$$1 \ 2 \ 3 \ 4 \ 5 \ 6 \ 7 \ 8 \ 9 = 100$$

'I don't quite follow,' said the editor.

'It's art,' said Ermine. 'You're not supposed to follow it. Anyway, this is the enigmas and puzzles column. It's meant to be enigmatic and puzzling.'

'But it's wrong,' the editor insisted.

'What's wrong?'

'The sum. It says that one hundred and twenty-three million, four hundred and fifty-six thousand, seven hundred and eighty-nine is equal to one hundred. I don't think that's right. Can't you change it?'

'No!' said Ermine. 'The paint's dried now.' A thought

struck her. 'I suppose I could let you have a bed instead... or a tent, or a stuffed parrot –'

'No, I like the board,' said the editor hurriedly. 'Why don't you paint a few mathematical symbols in the gaps between the digits, to make it right?'

'Now *I* don't follow.'

The editor rapidly sketched his concept on a piece of paper. 'Like this!'

$$1 + 23 + 45 + 6 + 7 + 8 + 9 = 100$$

'I see,' said Ermine. 'Except,' she went on, thumbing the calculator function of her mobile phone, 'doesn't that add up to 99?'

'Good point, Stacy. Can we make the sum add up to 100 if we use minus signs as well as plus signs?'

••

Answer on page 86

NOT ANOTHER BLOODY PARTRIDGE

Day one

'Oh, that's so sweet of him,' gushed Belinda. 'Look what my true love has sent me for Christmas! Isn't it just darling?'

'Some kind of bird?' hazarded her friend Emily. 'In a bush?'

'Silly! It's a partridge in a pear tree.'

'Well, that's novel.'

Day two

'Oh, wow! Emily, look! Two lovebirds!'

'I think they're turtle doves, Belinda.'

'And another partridge!'

Day three

'I hope the three hens are good layers,' said Emily. 'But why has he sent you more doves and another partridge? You've got three partridges, four doves, and three hens.'

'I'm sure my true love knows what he's doing,' said Belinda defensively.

Day four

'Another bloody partridge?'

'Yes, but you have to admit that the four calling birds are nice, Emily.'

'They're actually colly birds. Blackbirds.'

'I'm starting to see your point about the partridges. And the doves. And the hens.'

'If this goes on, you'll have an awful lot of birds. Twelve partridges, for starters. Twenty-two doves.'

'True. I wonder which species of bird I'll have the biggest number of?'

'No idea. But I think you ought to give *him* the bird.'

After the 12 days of Christmas, what species of bird will Belinda have the largest number of?

● ●

Answer on page 87

WHICH HAT IS WHOSE?

Every Friday afternoon, the committee of the Hardleigh Bothering Women's Institute meets in the village café for tea and scones. The committee members are Mrs Black, Mrs Brown, Mrs Green and Mrs White.

On this particular occasion, each lady wore a hat.

'What a coincidence!' said Mrs White.

'What is?' said Mrs Green, suspiciously.

'The colours of our hats are the same as our names!' Mrs White said. 'One black, one brown, one green, and one white!'

'True, but my hat isn't the same colour as my name,' Mrs Brown pointed out, sipping delicately from her teacup.

'No – but you *are* wearing the hat whose colour is the name of the person who's wearing the hat whose colour is the name of the person who's wearing the hat whose colour is your name,' said Mrs Black.

There was a silence while the other members of the committee digested this convoluted remark.

'True,' Mrs Brown finally conceded, her voice muffled by scone and jam. 'And the same goes for you, Mrs Black.'

'And for Mrs White,' said Mrs Green. All the ladies nodded their agreement.

What colour was Mrs Green's hat?

Answer on page 87

THE MONASTERY GARDEN

The Number Monks of Wuntumenni live their lives according to strict principles of numerology. The abbot and the deacon were engaged in building the new prayer patio in the Garden of Peerless Squares.

'It shall be just like the old patio,' said the abbot. 'But with more tiles.'

'The traditional form requires 25 tiles, arranged in a 5x5 square,' said the deacon. 'A square patio composed of a square number of square tiles.'

'Since each tile measured one metre by one metre, the perimeter of the old patio was 20 metres,' said the abbot.

'I must admit,' said the deacon, 'that the numerological significance of the perimeter escapes me.'

'Then be enlightened, my son,' said the abbot. 'As our founder P'tagras remarked, the same 25 tiles can be divided into two groups, each of which forms a rectangle with that exact same perimeter.'

'I see,' said the deacon. 'I can take 16 of the tiles to form a 2x8 rectangle, and the other nine tiles form a 1x9 rectangle. Each also has a perimeter of 20 metres.'

'That is so. How can we do the same, but starting with a larger square?'

'We could double all the numbers. One hundred tiles in a 10x10 square, which split into 64 arranged in a 4x16 rectangle and the remaining 36 in a 2x18 rectangle – all with a perimeter of 40 metres.'

'You forget that elegance of proportion demands an odd number of tiles in total.'

The deacon thought for a few moments. 'In that case, the next largest number of tiles that could be employed is –'

What is the next largest number of tiles?

Answer on page 87

THE RIDDLE OF THE VANISHING CAMEL

Three Arabian princes gathered around the aged Sheikh's deathbed to witness their father's final bequests. The family had fallen on hard times, but the Sheikh still owned a number of fine camels.

'To you, my eldest son Fuad, I bequeath half my camels,' intoned the Sheikh. 'Use them wisely.'

'I will, O my father,' said the boy, close to tears.

'Next, to my second son Khalid, I bequeath one third of my camels.' In a hoarse voice, Khalid thanked the old man for his generosity.

'Finally, to my youngest son Ahmed – one ninth of my camels.' Ahmed had not expected anything, and found himself unable to speak, so strong was his emotion.

Within the night, the Sheikh was dead. Fuad, now the new Sheikh, was in charge of carrying out his father's bequest. He sent a servant to count the camels.

'*Seventeen*?' The servant bowed low and confirmed the number. 'How in the name of the Dust Devils of the Dismal Desert can I divide 17 camels? I cannot split a camel like a loaf of bread. A dead camel is of no use to anybody save the glue-makers.'

'Father would consult the Wise One,' suggested Khalid tentatively.

'Make it so.'

The Wise One (the local name for 'mathematician') considered the problem carefully, making inscrutable notes in the margin of a small textbook of number theory and muttering to himself. He then instructed the Sheikh's servant to bring in his own, somewhat disreputable, camel.

'How will this help?' asked Fuad sarcastically. 'The problem is unchanged!'

Without a word, the Wise One led nine camels – half of 18 – and handed their reins to Fuad. Next, he handed six camels – one third of 18 – to Khalid. Then Ahmed received two camels – one ninth of 18. Only one camel was left: the Wise One's own mangy beast. He clambered on to its back and rode away in silence, leaving the three princes to contemplate the miracle.

It's a classic puzzle, and your first task is to explain why it works. Your second, less classic task, concerns a second Sheikh who also had three sons, and also left half his camels to his first son and one third to his second son, but left one seventh of his camels to the third son. Again the Wise One's single camel unlocked the riddle. So: how many camels did the second Sheikh have?

Answer on page 88

PIGFUNGLER'S SYNDROME

'I'm becoming concerned about the incidence of Pigfungler's syndrome,' said the Acrimonian health minister. 'What are the latest figures, Bertram?'

'Out of a total population of 200 million, it is estimated that half a million Acrimonian citizens suffer from PS, minister. The figure is based on random testing of a representative sample, but it's probably quite accurate.'

The minister stared at him. 'But that doesn't tell us *which* people have the disease, Bertram! We must initiate a programme of testing for all citizens!'

'The most accurate test available was devised by Professor Gnutter's team,' his secretary said. 'It detects 90 per cent of cases among those individuals who do have PS, and gives false positives for only 1 per cent of those individuals who do not.'

'That's good, isn't it?' said the minister brightly. 'We must go ahead immediately with a crash programme to test everybody!'

Bertram tugged at his ear, as if deep in thought. 'I'm not sure that's wise, minister.'

'Why ever not, man?'

'Well… you promised in your radio broadcast last week that you wouldn't alarm people with wrong diagnoses. You said that you would only institute a full-scale testing programme if the rate of false positives – the proportion of people wrongly tested positive for PS out of the total number that test positive – was less than 20 per cent.'

'So? Professor Gnutter's test clearly performs a lot better than that!'

Bertram grimaced. 'Er – I'm not sure that it does, actually, minister.'

Who is right: Bertram or the minister?

•••

Answer on page 88

BIG UGLYVILLE SUBWAY

'We're gonna build a subway,' the mayor stated. 'We got nine shopping malls in Uglyville, and we're gonna link 'em all together so that people can get from one to another without using their cars an' pollutin' our beautiful city.'

He pointed to a map on the wall which showed the nine malls. They formed a perfect 3x3 square array, like this:

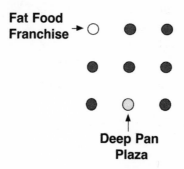

'Great idea, boss,' said the city engineer.

'We'll call it the Big Uglyville Subway,' said the mayor. 'I can see the ads: let the BUS take the strain!'

'Uh – smart thinking, boss. I'll get the boys working on some plans.'

'Yeah. I wanna single line that runs from Fat Food Franchise to Deep Pan Plaza, with a station at every mall.'

'How about this?' asked the city engineer, sketching rapidly on a legal pad.

'Nah. For starters, it doesn't end at Deep Pan Plaza. And it's got four bends. The Rekkit construction company tells me that straight tunnels are easy, but bends, they cost. The budget allows for no more than three bends.'

The city engineer scratched his head. 'Can the line cross itself?'

'Sure. We can put in a stop-light. But not at a station, that'd confuse folks.'

What plan did the city engineer come up with?

Answer on page 88

Answers

Rekkit must start by demolishing a 5x3 region at the left of the zone. That leaves DynaMight with a remaining zone that is square. Whatever choice they now make, the result is no longer square (unless they foolishly demolish everything, including the toxic block). Now Rekkit again chooses to make the remaining zone square, and eventually DynaMight is left with just the toxic block (a 1x1 square) and has no choice but to demolish that.

If Rekkit makes any other opening choice, DynaMight can use the same technique to force Rekkit to risk losing money.

THE GREEN SOCKS MURDER

The murderer is Mr Brown. In fact, by eliminating impossible combinations, Holmes was able to deduce that: Green wore white shirt, green shorts, brown socks; Brown wore brown shirt, white shorts, green socks; White wore green shirt, brown shorts, white socks.

YO-HO-HO AND A DEMOCRATIC VOTE

Pewter (P10) should propose to keep 96 gold pieces for himself, to give one gold piece to each of P8, P6, P4 and P2, and none to the odd-numbered pirates.

To explain: if only P1 to P4 remain, then P4 needs 50 per cent of the vote, so again he needs to bring exactly one other pirate on board. The minimum bribe he can use is one gold piece, and he can offer this to P2 since P2 will get nothing if P4's proposal fails and P3's is voted on. So P4's proposed allocation is:

P1 P2 P3 P4
0 1 0 99

P5 needs to bribe two pirates. The minimum bribe he can use is one gold piece to each of them, and the only way he can succeed with this number is to propose the allocation:

```
P1  P2  P3  P4  P5
1   0   1   0   98
```

The analysis proceeds in a similar manner, with each proposal being uniquely prescribed by giving the proposer the greatest possible number of coins, subject to enough bribes to ensure a favourable vote, until we get to P10:

```
P1  P2  P3  P4  P5
0   1   0   1   0
P6  P7  P8  P9  P10
1   0   1   0   96
```

HAT TRICK

Betty was right. There are eight different hat assignments, all equally likely: WWW, WWB, WBW, WBB, BWW, BWB BBW, BBB. In two of them, all three hats are the same colour. In the other six cases, two hats are one colour and one hat is the opposite colour. Betty's strategy is this: any player who sees two hats of the same colour states that their own hat is the opposite colour; everyone else passes. If all hats are the same, they lose. Otherwise – six cases out of eight, three chances in four – they win.

Of course, they could agree a secret signalling system, but that's not in the spirit of the puzzle. And it's surprising that they can do this well without one.

SQUARED SQUARES

1. Moroń's squared rectangle (below)
2. Duijvestijn's square (bottom)

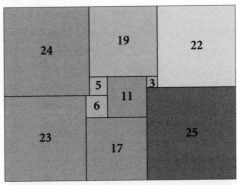

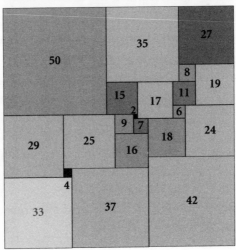

NUMEROMANCER

Here is one of the 12 special solutions, where the six outer points add up to 26.

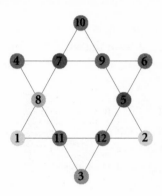

PROPORTIONAL MISREPRESENTATION

The run-off should pit the Autocrats against the Paternalists. If the DicDems take part in the run-off, they will be eliminated by 98 per cent to 2 per cent whichever party opposes them. However, if the Autocrats are run off against the Paternalists, the Autocrats will win by 51 per cent to 49 per cent. With the Paternalists eliminated, 51 per cent of the voters then prefer the DicDems to the Autocrats.

FLATLAND CHESS

1. The second player can always win in Flatland draughts.

2. In Flatland chess, the first player can force a win.

The (only) correct opening is to move the knight.
Number the cells 1–8 from the left. White moves first.
R=rook, N=knight, K=king, x='takes,' -- ='moves' *=check,
†=mate

W	B	W	B	W	B	W	B	W	B	W
N--4	RxN	RxR	N--5	RxN†						
	R--5	K--2	R--6	NxR†						
			RxN	RxR	N--5	RxN†				
	N--5	NxR*	K--7	R--4	KxN	K--2	K--7	RxN†		
				N--3*	K--2	N--1	N--8†			
						N--5	N--8	KxN	RxN†	

CHANCE ENCOUNTER

None of those answers were right. The correct answer is that
Patsy and Mark's chance of winning is 1 in 3. Maddox knew
this, and *he* cleaned up. To see why, consider the first card
chosen. Whichever one it is, the second card is chosen from
the remaining three, and exactly one card out of those three
matches the colour of the first.

So the chance of a match is 1 in 3.

THE ROUTE OF THE MATTER

There is a route, but Alice was also right in a sense.
The letters in the phrase NO WAY I'M SURE spell out a
route (go to successive towns with those initials).

SLOANE ARRANGER

Four pieces are sufficient. The carpet can be cut in a number
of ways – too many to note here. Below is one example.

THE BLEEPING SQUARESBOURNES

The kids' ages can be represented as a, a+b, a+2b, ... a+8b.

So $a^2 + (a+b)^2 + (a+2b)^2 + ... + (a+8b)^2 = c^2$ where a, b, c are all whole numbers.

That is, $9a^2 + 72ab + 204b^2 = c^2$.

The only solution with realistic ages is a=2, b=3, c=48.

Squozzy is 48. The children are 2, 5, 8, 11, 14, 17, 20, 23 and 26.

LEADER OF THE PACK

Any solution packs the box with six crates and three holes, each hole being a one-foot cube. The key is to work out where to put the *holes*.

Imagine dividing the crate into three layers, each 3x3x1: a total of 9 one-foot cubes. Each box meets such a layer in an even number of one-foot cubes – 0, 2, or 4. Since 9 is odd, there has to be at least one hole in each horizontal layer; since there are three layers, only one hole can occur in any layer. The same reasoning applies if we divide the crate from side to side or front to back. The easiest way to do this (though not the only one) is if the three holes occupy a long diagonal of the cube.

Then the boxes pretty much place themselves.

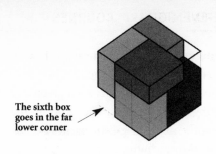

The sixth box goes in the far lower corner

SQUARE-DANCING DILEMMA

CIRCUMNAVIGATIONOLOGY

The obituary writer was wrong – Elaine's average speed was not 25 knots. She took 18,000 ÷ 30 = 600 hours to reach Sydney and 18,000 ÷ 20 = 900 hours to return, a total of 1,500 hours (and an aggregate speed of 24 knots).

Each way, Arthur took 18,000 ÷ 24.5 = 734.7 hours, a total of 1,469.4 hours.

So Arthur won.

TRAIN OF EVENTS

The red train remains in one section at all times; the green train is uncoupled and reconnected.

1. Disconnect the coupling between green coaches five and six, numbering from the front. The red train then moves west, pushing the other 21 green coaches before it, until it is clear of Central Interchange.

2. The green engine pulls the five disconnected coaches far enough east to leave the red train room.

3. Red reverses eastwards through the south line. It drops off the last seven green coaches on that line.

4. Red moves west along the north line until it is clear of Central Interchange.

5. Red reverses back along the south line, picking up the seven green coaches. It stops to drop off its last seven green coaches on the south line, then continues to reverse until the green coaches at its rear meet the green train and can be linked to it.

6. It drops these off and repeats the same manoeuvre twice more.

PUNK POODLE PARADE

The shortest sequence takes five moves.

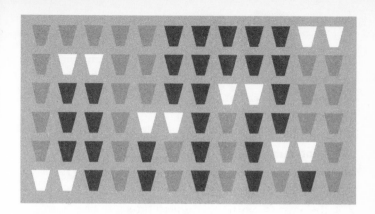

ORDER INTO CHAOS
....

Here's one way:

> **ORDER**
> **OLDER**
> **ELDER**
> **EIDER**
> **CIDER**
> **CODER**
> **CODES**
> **CORES**
> **CORPS**
> **COOPS**
> **CHOPS**
> **CHAPS**
> **CHAOS**

TRICKY WICKET

Chuckit's eleventh batsman scored half their remaining runs plus three halves of a run – ie three runs. Working backwards to the eighth batsman, this gives Chuckit a total score of 12.

Wackingham's eleventh batsman scored half of their remaining runs plus half a run – ie one run. Working backwards, this gives Wackingham a total score of 11.

So Chuckit won.

PROPITIOUSLY PROPORTIONED PYRAMID

Pythagoras's theorem states that for a right-angled triangle, the sum of the squares of the two shorter sides is equal to the square of the longest side.

Therefore, in our pyramid:

$a^2 + x^2 = c^2$ and $x^2 + x^2 = b^2$.

It follows that $a^2 + b^2/2 = c^2$.

But we are told that:

$a = b - 1$ and $c = b + 1$.

So, $(b - 1)^2 + b^2/2 = (b + 1)^2$

$b^2 = 8b$, therefore $b = 8$.

The lengths a, b, c must be in the proportions 7, 8, 9.

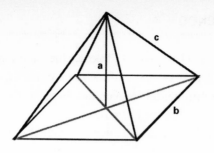

THE MERCHANT OF SAMARKAND

If each son must get 3.5 barrels of oil, then they must receive an odd number of half-full barrels. As they can only have a maximum of 3 identical barrels, each son can either receive 1 or 3. Since there are 7 half-full barrels in total, they have to be split between the sons in lots of 3, 3 and 1.

The total amount of oil each son gets must equal 3.5 barrels. The two sons with 3 half-full barrels already have 1.5 barrels of oil, so each needs 2 full barrels. The son with 1 half-full barrel needs 3 full barrels.

In order for each son to have 7 barrels in total, the son with 1 half-full barrel must get 3 empty barrels, and the other sons must receive 2 each. So the barrels are divided like this:

	Full	Half	Empty
Son	2	3	2
Son	3	1	3
Son	2	3	2

HIGH AFTERNOON

The hands meet 11 times in 12 hours, at equally spaced intervals. Each interval is therefore $\frac{1}{11}$ of 12 hours, which is one hour five minutes 27 $\frac{3}{11}$ seconds. So the gunfight takes place 27 $\frac{3}{11}$ seconds after five past one.

CAT O'SEVEN TAILS

There were four felinoids. The largest number that is not a multiple of five plus a multiple of seven is 23. Removing Sooty, there are 22 felinoid tails. The only possible combination is $(3\times5)+(1\times7)=22$.

So there were three *Catticus fatticus* and one *Pussius fussius*.

DIGITAL CENTURY

$$123 - 45 - 67 + 89 = 100$$

There are a number of alternative answers. Another possibility, for example, is:

$$- 1 + 2 - 3 + 4 + 5 + 6 + 78 + 9 = 100$$

NOT ANOTHER BLOODY PARTRIDGE

The largest total of birds, over the 12 days of Christmas, is 42 geese a-laying, equalled by 42 swans a-swimming.

WHICH HAT IS WHOSE?

You can solve this by trial and error, or as follows: imagine each lady is holding her own hat in her left hand, and the hat which is the same colour as her name in her right hand. Mrs Brown is then part of a closed ring of only three ladies. Mrs Black and Mrs White also belong to a ring of three ladies, so they are in the same ring as Mrs Brown. Mrs Green is left out, holding her hat with both hands, so her hat must be green.

THE MONASTERY GARDEN

The next largest number of tiles is 169. Checking the perimeters and areas of all possible rectangles reveals that there are no appropriate combinations for squares of 7x7, 9x9 or 11x11. However, a 13x13 square (of 169 tiles) can be split into an 8x18 rectangle (of 144 tiles) and 1x25 rectangle (of 25 tiles). All of these have a perimeter of 52 metres.

THE RIDDLE OF THE VANISHING CAMEL

The sum of $\frac{1}{2}$, $\frac{1}{3}$, and $\frac{1}{9}$ is not 1, but $\frac{17}{18}$. The extra camel makes up the total so that the division is possible; the missing $\frac{1}{18}$ accounts precisely for the Wise One's camel.

The sum of $\frac{1}{2}$, $\frac{1}{3}$, and $\frac{1}{7}$ is $\frac{41}{42}$. By similar reasoning, the second Sheikh had 41 camels.

PIGFUNGLER'S SYNDROME

Bertram is right. Out of 500,000 people with PS, 450,000 will test positive. Out of 199,500,000 people not suffering from PS, 1,995,000 will test positive. The test will give a false positive in 1.995 million cases out of a total of 2.445 million, a failure rate slightly more than 81 per cent.

BIG UGLYVILLE SUBWAY

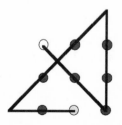

Notes

Notes